"There is an old proverb that says 'Thoughts disentangle themselves when passing over the lips and through the finger tips.' The 17:18 Series, which encourages us to actually write out the words of Scripture, will be a tremendous tool in putting that proverb into action in our daily lives. I am happy to commend this project."

–Jerry Bridges, a longtime staff member of the Navigators and author of *The Pursuit of Holiness*

"Several years ago I read an article about copying the Scriptures by hand. I tried it with the Pastoral Epistles, writing out all three books with a fountain pen in my journal, and found it a profitable exercise. I am glad to see this series of journals appear, and I hope they are widely used."

–Donald S. Whitney, Associate Professor of Biblical Spirituality, The Southern Baptist Theological Seminary, Louisville

The 17:18 Series

The Book of
Matthew

Joel R. Beeke and Rob Wynalda

This book belongs to:

Cathy T Burns

Given by: Hannah Lightfoot

Date: 5/17/2021

Matthew

Published by
Reformation Heritage Books
2965 Leonard St.
Grand Rapids, MI 49525
616-977-0889 / Fax 616-285-3246
e-mail: orders@heritagebooks.org
website: www.heritagebooks.org

ISBN 978-1-60178-333-2

Cover Design: Bethany Sanderson and Steve Coy
Journible® Design: Rob Wynalda

Thanks Nicole

hy the 17:18 series?

Deuteronomy 17, Moses is leaving final instructions ncerning the future of Israel. As a prophet of God, oses foretells of when Israel will place a king over the tion (v. 14). In verses 16 & 17, he lists items that the ng could not do as king. In verse 18, he transitions to hat he should do as king.

he king is commanded not to simply acquire a copy of e law (the entire book of Deuteronomy) from the "scroll blishing house," but to handwrite his own copy of the law. he purpose of such a copy written by his own hand was that:

* he would read it
* he would learn to fear the Lord
* he would obey the commands of God
* his heart would not become proud
* he would not turn to the right or the left from following the law (Prov. 4:27)
* also, his sons would serve in the kingdom after him. (Deut. 17:19, 20)

hirty-four hundred years later, educators are 'iscovering" that students who physically write out their tes by hand have a much greater retention rate than ose who simply hear or visually read the information. pparently, God knew this to be true for the kings of rael also.

rom such understanding came the conception of this series books.

ave a great time writing and learning the Word of God,

ob Wynalda
omans 1:16

he Purpose of the Journible®

ngagement:

he Journible® is a profoundly simple attempt to aid a erson's ability to engage the Word of God by slowing own the process of simply reading the text. The book is rganized so that the "scribe" can slowly and thoughtfully ngage the text while leaving plenty of room to write mments and questions about the text (Deuteronomy 17:18; salm 119; 2 Timothy 3:16, 17).

egacy:

ournibles® provide a legacy to pass on from one generation the next. The Journible® creates an opportunity for one eneration to communicate in writing to the next generation eir insights and personal applications of the text Deuteronomy 6).

ow to use this book

his book is organized so that the scribe (you) will andwrite your very own copy of Matthew. You will be riting the text of the Bible only on the right-hand page the book. This should make for easier writing and also lows ample space on the left page of your open text to rite your own notes and comments. From time to time a estion or word will be lightly printed on the left page; ese questions are to aid in further study, but should not terfere with your own notes and comments. This means at you are encouraged not only to write your own "copy" the Bible, but also to write your own notes concerning e text.

es, we are setting aside our mass-produced Gutenberg ibles and attempting to get back to the simple handwritten opy of the text.

Notes

Matthew

ho wrote the book of Matthew?

hen was the book of Matthew written and for what purpose?

Notes

(1) Why is the genealogy of Jesus important?

(2) Why does this genealogy start with Abraham?

(5) Why does the genealogy include Gentiles like Rahab (KJV Rachab) and Ruth?

(6) Why does it mention David's adultery with the wife o[f] Uriah (KJV Urias)?

Notes

(11) Why is the exile to Babylon mentioned in Christ's genealogy

(13) Why is it significant that God continued to bless the line of David in men like Zerubbabel (KJV Zorobabel) after the return from exile (Hag. 2:23)?

(16) "Christ" is a title meaning "anointed." What is Jesus anointed to be? (See Ex. 28:41; 1 Kings 19:16.)

Notes

(18) What other women in the Bible experienced a miraculous conception of a child?

(19) What does this show about Joseph's character?

(21) Why was He named "Jesus"?

(23) How is Christ "God with us"?

(24) Why would it have been hard for Joseph to obey?

Matthew 1:18-24

Notes

Matthew 1:25

5

Notes

(1) Look up Herod the Great. What kind of man was this king

(2) Why would the wise men worship Christ?

(3) Why would Christ's birth trouble Herod?

(6) Where does this quote come from? What else did the prophecy say?

Notes

(9) Why would a star be associated with Christ? (See Nu. 24:17; Rev. 22:16.)

(11) Why are these three gifts offered to Jesus? (See Ex. 30:23–26, 34–35; Song 3:6; Isa. 60:6.)

(12) Does God normally reveal truth through dreams today? Why or why not?

Matthew 2:8-13

Notes

(15) Where was this prophesied in Scripture?

(16) What does this reveal about Herod?

(18) What is the context of this quotation in Jeremiah 31?

Notes

(21) How might these dangers and moves affect Jesus as a child

(22) Look up Herod Archelaus. Who was he?

(23) How does this verse shed light on Isaiah 53?

Matthew 2:20-23

0

1

2

3

Notes

(1) Who is John the Baptist? How does he fit into the story of Christ?

(2) What does "repent" mean? Why are the kingdom of heaven and repentance mentioned together?

(4) Like whom did John dress? (See 2 Kings 1:8.) Why? (See 11:14

(5) How does this compare with the Great Commission (Acts 1:8)?

(6) What was the purpose of baptism and confessing sins?

(8) What is the fruit of repentance?

Matthew 3:1-8

Notes

(10) What does it mean that the ax is at the base of the tree?

(11) What is the difference between the two baptisms?

(12) A fan or winnowing fork separates the grain from the chaff. What does this metaphor mean?

Matthew 3:9-14

Notes

(15) Why was it fitting for Christ to be baptized? How does His baptism "fulfill all righteousness"?

(16) What happened when the Spirit descended upon Jesus? (See Isa. 11:2; 61:1.)

(17) How do the Father's words help us to trust in Christ?

5

6

7

Notes

(1) Compare Christ's temptation to that of Adam and Eve (Gen. 3

(2) What special times of "forty" are there in the Old Testament

(4) What is the context of the quote Jesus is using?

(7) What does it mean to tempt or test the Lord? How does this apply today?

Matthew 4:1-7

Notes

(9) How can Satan promise this? (See John 14:30.)

(10) Which scripture did Jesus use for His rebuttal of Satan?

(11) How do angels relate to Christ and His people? (See Heb. 1:14.)

(12–17) Why did Jesus begin His public ministry in Galilee? (See Isa. 9:1–7.)

(13) Find this area on a map.

(15) What else did Isaiah prophesy in that context?

Matthew 4:8-15

Notes

(16) What is the shadow of death? How is Christ the ligh

(17) How similar is Jesus' message to that of John?

(19) What does "follow me" teach about true ministers? How about "fishers of men"?

(22) How did they respond to Christ's call? What does thi say about Jesus?

Matthew 4:16-22

6

7

8

9

0

1

2

Notes

(23) What did Jesus' healings reveal about Him?

(25) Why were Gentiles from the Decapolis coming to Jesus

3

4

5

Notes

(1–2) What is one reason why Christ came? (See Deut. 18:15; John 4:25.)

(3) What does it mean to be poor in spirit?

(5) Give an example of meekness.

(7) How does mercy act? (See Luke 10:30–37.)

(9) What does it mean to be children of God?

Matthew 5:1-10

Notes

(11) What does "for my sake" mean?

(13) How should Christians be like salt?

(16) How should Christians be like light?

(17) How does the Lord Jesus relate to the Old Testament?

Notes

(19) What are the commandments that Jesus is referring to?
(See vv. 21, 27, 33.)

(20) What was wrong with the righteousness of the Pharisees?
(See 6:2, 5, 16.)

(22) Why is sinful anger or insult a crime worthy of hell fire?
(See 1 John 3:15.)

Matthew 5:18-23

8

9

0

1

2

3

Notes

(24) What is Christ's point about leaving your gift at the altar

(27–28) Is Christ contradicting the Ten Commandments, adding to them, or applying their true meaning to the heart Why do you say that?

(30) Is Jesus expecting people to remove their eyes and cu their hands off? If not, what does He expect?

Matthew 5:24-30

4

5

6

7

8

9

0

Notes

(32) In what situation does Jesus allow for divorce?

(34) In this context what does Jesus mean when he says [cut off] not swear?

(38) What is the Lord Jesus quoting?

Notes

(39) Is Christ changing the law?

(42) Does this require doing everything that anyone asks of you? Why or why not?

(45) What does this reveal about God's kindness?

Matthew 5:39-46

Notes

(48) In verses 43–48 what does it mean to be perfect?

Notes

(1) Why would doing good for men to see forfeit your reward from God?

(3) What does it mean not to have the right hand know what the left hand is doing?

(5) What makes a person a hypocrite?

Matthew 6:1-6

Notes

(7) What are vain repetitions?

(9) What does "hallowed" mean?

(10) What is God's kingdom? (See 6:13; 12:28; 13:43; 25:34.) Why should we pray for it to come?

(12) How are sins like debts?

(14) How does God forgiving us relate to us forgiving others?

Matthew 6:7-15

Notes

(16) What is fasting? Should we do it today?

(18) How should the Father seeing in secret shape the Christian life?

(20) What is heavenly treasure? Why is it important to focus on heavenly rather than on earthly treasure?

(21) How do you know what your treasure is?

(22) What is the benefit of a single, or clear, eye?

Notes

(24) What is mammon? How does one serve it?

(25) Are you breaking the teachings of Jesus by working for a living? Why or why not?

(26) How does the Father's care for birds help the Christian to trust Him?

(30) When will the Father clothe His children in glory (13:43)? How can that give them peace today?

Matthew 6:24-30

Notes

(33) How does one pursue the kingdom of God?

Matthew 6:31-34

Notes

(1) What did Christ mean by "judge"?

(3) What is the lesson of the beam, or log?

(6) What does the dog represent? (See Pss. 22:16; 59:5–
What is Christ's point?

Matthew 7:1-8

Notes

(9–11) What does this tell us about how a child of God should view the Father?

(12) How did Christ summarize the Old Testament teaching of how to treat people?

(13) What is the strait, or narrow, gate?

(16) What is a sign of a false teacher?

Notes

(17) What is good fruit? (See 3:8, 10.)

(20) How would you put this in your own words?

(21) Why is obedience to God's will necessary to enter the kingdom

(23) Why would the Lord say "I never knew you"?

Notes

(26) Whom does the foolish builder represent?

(29) What made Christ's teaching so amazing? How can m
teach like that today?

Matthew 7:25-29

25

26

27

28

29

Notes

(2) Why is it always good when we are facing trials to te
the Lord that if He wills, He is able to help us?

(3) What is the significance of Jesus' healing a leper?

(4) Why did Jesus require this? (See Lev. 14:1–4.)

(7) What does Christ's willingness to heal the servant of
Roman centurion show about Him?

Notes

(8–9) What was the centurion saying about Jesus?

(12) Who are the children of the kingdom? Why would they be cast out?

Notes

(17) What Scripture is quoted here? How does it apply to Christ's healings?

(20) Why did Christ say this to a man who promised to follow Him anywhere?

Matthew 8:14-21

Notes

(22) Why must following Christ take priority over family? (See 10:37.)

(24) How does Christ's sleeping show us His humanness?

(27) What is the answer to their question?

(29) What do the demons mean by saying "torment us befor the time"?

Matthew 8:22-29

2

3

4

5

6

7

8

9

Notes

(32) What does the action of the pigs tell us about demons

(34) What makes this a sad verse?

Matthew 8:30-34

30

31

32

33

34

Notes

(1–8) What do Christ's miracles teach us about forgivenes of sins?

(2) Why does the Lord Jesus forgive the man's sin while healing him?

(3) What is blasphemy? What is the punishment if one is guilty of it?

(5) What is the answer to Jesus' question?

Matthew 9:1-8

Notes

(9) What does it teach about Christ that He called a tax collector?

(11) What was the significance of eating with publicans an[d] sinners?

(13) What was lacking in the Pharisees' righteousness?

Matthew 9:9-14

Notes

(15) Why would Christians fast?

(17) What do these parables mean?

(20) How would the woman's bleeding have affected her life? (See Lev. 15:19–27.)

Matthew 9:15-20

5

6

7

8

9

0

Notes

(22) How did the woman exhibit faith in Christ?

(25) What does this miracle show us about the Lord Jesus

(27) What is the significance of the phrase "Son of David"

Matthew 9:21-28

2

3

4

5

6

7

8

Notes

(29) Why did they need to believe to be healed?

(30–31) Why did Christ discourage some people from publicizing His miracles?

(35) What is the gospel of the kingdom?

Matthew 9:29-35

9

0

1

2

3

4

5

Notes

(37–38) Who are the laborers? What is the harvest? Why should we pray?

6

7

8

Notes

(1–2) What is one distinguishing mark of an apostle? (See also v. 8.)

(3–4) Matthew was a tax collector for the Romans, but Simon was an anti-Roman zealot (Luke 6:15). Why would Christ choose both?

(5) Why did Christ not yet send the apostles to other nations

(6) Why did the Lord call people "lost sheep"?

Matthew 10:1-9

Notes

(10) What does Christ's saying about the workman or laborer teach us about the Christian ministry? (See 1 Cor. 9:13–14; 1 Tim. 5:17–18.)

(12) Why is Christian hospitality important for missions? (See 3 John 5–8.)

(15) Why does Jesus refer to Sodom?

Notes

(18–19) How would Jewish and Gentile leaders treat the apostle

(20) How did God help the apostles to testify before all me

(22) Why must a person endure to the end to be saved?

Notes

(25) Beelzebub is a name for Satan, based on a pagan g
(2 Kings 1:2). Why would they call Christ that? (See 9:34

(28) Whom should we not fear? Whom should we fear? Wh

(29–30) What is Jesus teaching about God's providence?

Matthew 10:25-31

Notes

(32) Why must we confess Christ before men? (See Rom. 10:

(34–36) How does the gospel bring a "sword"?

(38) What must we do to be Christ's disciples?
What does that mean?

Matthew 10:32-39

2

3

4

5

6

7

8

9

Notes

(40) What does the way we treat Christ's preachers reve about us?

(42) How does this promise encourage us to serve God?

Notes

(3) What does John's question show about how persecution can affect a believer's faith?

(5) What evidences did Jesus give that He is the Christ?

(7) What does it mean to be a reed shaken by the wind?

Notes

(10) What scripture is Jesus quoting? What does it mean?

(12) What kind of "violence" is necessary to enter the kingdom? (See Luke 13:24; 16:16.)

(14) How was John the Baptist like Elijah (KJV, Elias)?

Notes

(17) How was John's ministry a call to mourn, and Christ's coming a cause to dance?

(19) What is Jesus teaching when he says "wisdom is justified of her children"?

(21) Define "woe."

Notes

(24) What does "more tolerable" imply about judgment day

(25) Why do wise men reject the gospel, but some immatu
or foolish people receive it?

(27) What does this tell us about Christ's unique relationship with God? What does it teach about Christ's sovereignty in salvation?

3

4

5

6

7

8

Notes

(29) What is the rest that Jesus offers?

Notes

(1) Were the disciples stealing? (See Deut. 23:25.)

(3–4) How does the example of David justify the disciples taking grain on the Sabbath?

(6) What One greater than the temple was there?

(7) Why does God love mercy more than sacrifice?

(8) What does it imply about Christ that He is Lord of the Sabbath? (See Isa. 58:13.) What does it imply about the Sabbath? (See Rev. 1:10.)

Notes

(11) What principle is the Lord teaching about the Sabbath

(13–14) What two different kinds of religion do we see exemplified in Christ and the Pharisees?

Matthew 12:9-16

Notes

(17–21) How does Jesus fulfill each part of Isaiah's prophecy

(25) How does Christ disprove the charge that Satan empowers Him to cast out demons?

Matthew 12:17-25

7

8

9

0

2

3

4

5

Notes

(28) In what sense has the kingdom come already? (See Rom. 14:17.)

(29) What has Christ done to the devil?

(31) What is blasphemy against the Holy Spirit?

Matthew 12:26-32

6

7

8

9

0

1

2

Notes

(33–34) Why do people do and say evil things?

(36) For what will God call us to account on judgment day

(38–42) How is Christ greater than Jonah and Solomon?

(39) Why was it wrong to ask for a sign or miracle?

3

4

5

6

7

8

9

Notes

(41–42) Who will condemn many of Christ's hearers on judgment day? Why?

(44–45) How does this story show the state of the Pharisees and those like them?

0

1

2

3

4

Notes

5

6

7

8

9

0

Notes

(3) What is a parable?

(4–8) Outline the differences between the kinds of soil.

Matthew 13:1-10

Notes

(11) Why did Christ teach in parables?

(13–15) What is God's judgment on those whom He has not chosen?

Notes

(17) What great privilege did Christ's disciples have?

(19–22) What three spiritual obstacles stop people from benefiting from God's Word?

Notes

(23) What proves that a person has been saved by God's Word

(26) How do people see what is wheat and what are tares, or weeds?

(29–30) Why did the farmer not tear out the weeds immediately?

3

4

5

6

7

8

9

Notes

(32–33) What do the mustard seed and leaven teach abou
God's kingdom?

Matthew 13:30-35

0

1

2

3

4

5

Notes

(36) What opportunity do Christ's disciples have that the crowds do not?

(38–39) What are the field, good seed, tares (or weeds), enemy, harvest, and reapers?

(40) When will Christ separate the wicked and the righteous

(42) What will the Lord and His angels do with the wicked

(43) What will be the future of the righteous?

Matthew 13:36-43

6

7

8

9

0

2

3

Notes

(46) How is the kingdom like this pearl?

(50) Why will the wicked gnash their teeth?
(See Job 16:9; Acts 7:54.)

Matthew 13:44-51

4

5

6

7

8

9

0

1

Notes

(52) What did Christ say about the well-trained teacher of the kingdom?

(55) What do we learn about Christ's family here?

(58) What is the connection between mighty works and unbelie

Matthew 13:52-58

2

3

4

5

6

7

8

Notes

(1) Look up the tetrarch, Herod Antipas. What kind of man was h

(3–4) Why did Herod arrest John? How does this show John's faithfulness and courage?

(8–9) What does this reveal about the hearts of Herod and Herodias?

Notes

(12) How must this have affected John's disciples and Jesus?

(14) How did the Lord Jesus respond when He saw the crow

(16) Why did Christ tell His disciples to feed the crowd themselves?

Notes

(20) What does this miracle teach us about Christ? About serving Christ?

(23) How is Jesus an example to us here?

(25) How did the Lord Jesus show His divine power?

Notes

(28–31) How did Peter show the reality yet weakness of his faith in Christ?

(33) Why is it right to worship Jesus Christ?

Notes

Notes

(2) Why are the scribes and Pharisees concerned with washing hands? (See Mark 7:3–4.)

(5–6) How did the Lord criticize their traditionalism?

(7–8) What does God think of hypocrisy?

Notes

(9) What happens to worship if it is based on man's commands and not God's Word?

(11) How did the Lord criticize their concern about externa rituals?

(13–14) What did Christ say about all religion not createo by God's sovereign grace?

(16) Why did Christ rebuke Peter?

Notes

(22) Why would a Gentile woman seek help from the Son of David?

(24) Why didn't the Lord Jesus immediately grant her request?

Notes

(27) How does the woman's answer show her humility and fait

(28) How does this verse preach the fullness of the gospe

(31) What did Christ's power and mercy move people to d

Notes

(33) How does their question show they were slow to believe? (See 14:15–21.)

(36) Why should we thank God for our food? (See Ps. 136:25–26; 1 Tim. 4:4–5.)

(38) How many people did the Lord feed with seven loaves ar a few little fish? What does that teach us about His power?

Matthew 15:32-39

Notes

(3) What "signs of the times" should they have recognized

(4) What is the sign of Jonah? (See 12:39–41.)

(8) Why did Christ rebuke His disciples?

Notes

(12) What is the leaven of the Pharisees?

(15) What question did Jesus ask? Why is it the most important of all questions?

(16–17) How did Peter answer this question? How was he able to know this?

Notes

(19) Keys symbolize authority (Isa. 22:22; Rev. 1:18). What kind of authority did Christ give the leaders of the church?

(21) Why did the Lord say these things "must" happen? (See 20:28; 26:54.)

Matthew 16:17-22

Notes

(23) Why did Christ call Peter "Satan"?

(24) What does it mean to "take up his cross"?

(26) How valuable is your soul?

Matthew 16:23-28

3

4

5

6

7

8

Notes

(1–12) Why is the Transfiguration account situated between two prophecies of Christ's suffering and death? (See 16:21–23 and 17:22–23.)

(2) What did Christ reveal about Himself by shining like the sun? (See Ps. 84:11; Isa. 60:1, 19; Mal. 4:2.)

(4) Who are Moses and Elijah? What does their appearance with Jesus signify?

(5) How does God command us to respond to the glory of His beloved Son?

(7) If Christ is that glorious, why should they not be afraid

Matthew 17:1-8

Notes

(9) When were they permitted to speak about this vision?

(12–13) When did Elijah come?

Notes

(18) What does it show about Jesus that his disciples coul[d] not heal the boy, but Jesus did with a mere word?

(20) Why couldn't the disciples cast out the demon?

(23) How did the disciples respond when the Lord again predicted His death and resurrection?

Notes

(25) Who are the sons of the King? (See 13:43.)

(27) Peter would catch a fish with the exact amount of money in its mouth. What does this tell us about God's sovereignty?

Matthew 17:24-27

4

5

6

7

Notes

(1–4) What characteristics are there in a child that illustrate what believers should be like in their relationship to God?

(3) What is necessary to enter God's kingdom?

(4) Who is the greatest in the kingdom?

(6) What could be worse than having a massive stone hung around your neck and being drowned in the ocean?

(8–9) What is the Lord talking about through the metaphor of cutting off a hand?

Matthew 18:1-8

Notes

(11) Why did Christ come?

(14) Does this refer to the death of a child, or the damnation of a humble disciple of Christ? Why?

(15—17) What did Christ teach Christians to do if one of them sins?

Notes

(19) What promise did the Lord Jesus give His church?

(22) What did He teach us about forgiving each other?

Notes

(24) Ten thousand talents is an enormous debt only a king could pay (Est. 3:9). What is Christ teaching us about the guilt of our sins against God?

(26) What does the servant's promise to pay it all reveal about him?

(28) What is so offensive about the servant's actions here

3

4

5

6

7

8

9

Notes

(31) How does it affect others in the church if we do not forgive those who sin against us?

(34–35) What will the Father do to us if we do not forgive each other?

Matthew 18:30-35

Notes

(3) What question did they ask to test Jesus?

(4–5) What scriptures did Christ quote? Why did He base His teaching about marriage and divorce upon creation?

Notes

(9) What is the Lord Jesus' teaching about divorce?

(12) What does it mean to make oneself a eunuch for the kingdo

(14) What is Christ's heart toward children?

Notes

(17) Why did Christ challenge the man's view of goodness and call him to obey the law?

(19) What does it mean to love your neighbor as yourself?

(20) What is wrong with this man?

(22) Compare this man to the parables of the treasure and the pearl (13:44–46). What does this comparison reveal about him?

Matthew 19:16-22

Notes

(24) What is Christ's point about the camel?

(26) Why is salvation impossible for man? (See 15:13)

(29) What does forsaking property or family have to do with gaining eternal life? (See 10:37–39.)

Notes

(1) Who are the laborers in God's kingdom? What is their wor

(3–4) The "third hour" was about 9 a.m., a quarter of th way into the work day. How much might they have expecte for pay?

(6) At the "eleventh hour," only one hour remained to wor (v. 12). How much might they expect to be paid?

Matthew 20:1-7

Notes

(9) What does this payment reveal about the master?

(12) Was anyone treated unfairly?

(15) What do these two questions teach us about God?

Notes

(16) How does this parable illustrate the principle that the last will be first and the first last? (See also 19:30).

(18–19) Why does Jesus repeat this prediction?

(21) What would it mean to sit at the Lord's right and left han

(22) What does Jesus mean by a cup and baptism?

Notes

(26) How does one become great in Christ's kingdom?

(28) What does it mean to give His life as a "ransom for many

Notes

(30) Based on this verse, how would you define "mercy"?

(32) Why did Christ ask them this?

Matthew 20:30-34

Notes

(2) Why did the Lord Jesus intentionally enter Jerusalem in this way?

(5) What scripture is quoted here? What does it say in context?

(8) Why did they lay their garments under Him? (See Kings 9:12–13.)

Notes

(9) What scripture is quoted here? (See also v. 42.)

(12–13) Why did Jesus clear the merchants from the temp

(15) Why did the chief priest become angry?

(19) What did the fig tree symbolize? (See 3:8–10; Luke 13:6–

(21) What does the casting down of a mountain represent? (See 17:18–21; Ps. 46:2; Isa. 2:11–17; Jer. 51:25–29.)

Notes

(24–26) Why does Jesus answer a question with a question? How does His question expose their hypocrisy?

(29) What does "repented" mean? (See Acts 26:20.)

3

4

5

6

7

8

9

Notes

(31) How does the parable of the two sons illustrate the difference between repentant sinners and the Pharisees?

(33) Compare Christ's parable to Isaiah 5:1–7. What is the vineyard? What is the fruit?

Matthew 21:30-34

(35) Whom do the servants of the owner represent in thi
parable?

(38) What is Christ saying the Jewish leaders will do, ar
for what reason?

(42) Who is the stone that was rejected? How has it beer
honored?

5

6

7

8

9

0

2

Notes

(43) How were these words fulfilled in history?

3

4

5

6

Notes

(3–4) How is the gospel call like an invitation to a wedding feas

(5–6) What are two ways unbelievers respond to evangelism

(7) What was Christ threatening?

Notes

(9) What does this represent? (See 28:19.)

(11) What is meant by the wedding garment?

(13) Why was the man without wedding clothes cast into outer darkness?

(14) What is the difference between "called" and "chosen"

Notes

(16) Why did the Pharisees praise Christ?

(18) Why are they wicked?

(21) What do we owe to civil rulers? What do we owe to Go

Notes

(24–28) How did the Sadducees try to make the resurrection seem ridiculous?

(30) How did they fail to know the power of God in raising the dead?

(31–32) How did they fail to know the implications of the Scriptures?

Matthew 22:24-31

Notes

(33) How did Christ's answer affect the crowd?

(37) What scripture did Christ quote? Why is it the greatest commandment?

(39) What does it mean to love your neighbor as yourself (See Luke 10:25–37.)

(40) Why do all God's laws depend on these two commandments?

Notes

(44) What scripture did Jesus quote?

(45) How would you answer Christ's question?

2

3

4

5

6

Notes

(3) How does Christ sum up the hypocrisy of the Pharisee

(4) How do legalists put burdens on people but give them no hel

(6–7) What did these religious leaders love?

Notes

(11) What is the essence of true greatness?

(13) How does legalistic teaching shut the kingdom of heav
to people?

(15) What does it mean to be a child of hell?

(16) How did the Pharisees justify breaking their oaths?

Notes

(19) In what sense were they fools and blind?

(21) Whom do frivolous oaths ultimately dishonor?

(23) What are the weightier things of the law?

Notes

(25) What does the metaphor of the cup mean?

(27–28) How are the Pharisees like beautiful tombs?

Matthew 23:25-30

Notes

(33) When Christ called them serpents, to whom did He compare them? (See Gen. 3:1; Luke 10:17–19.)

Notes

(37) What does Jerusalem deserve? Yet what does Jesus long to do for them?

Notes

(2) When was this prophecy fulfilled?

(3) What two questions did the disciples ask Christ?

(6–7) How should Christians respond to wars, famines, epidemics, and earthquakes?

Notes

(9) How will the world treat Christ's followers?

(11–12) Should we expect truth and godliness to win the whole world?

(14) What must happen before Christ returns?

(15–18) What is the abomination of desolation? (See Dan. 9:27; 11:31; Luke 21:20.) What did Christ instruct believers in Judea to do when it came?

Matthew 24:9-18

Notes

(22) Who are the elect? (See 22:14; 24:24, 31; 1 Peter 1:1—

(24) How do false prophets convince people to listen to them? (See 2 Thess. 2:9.)

(27) How will Christ's coming be like lightning?

Notes

(28) What do the carcass and scavengers mean? (See Ezek. 39:17–20; Rev. 19:17–18.)

(29–31) What will happen at the end of the age?

(32) Why is Jesus speaking about a fig tree? (See 21:19.)

Notes

(35) What does Christ tell us about His Word?

(37–39) How is Noah's flood like the coming of Christ?

(42) Why must Christians always watch for Christ's retur

Notes

(44–45) How does one become ready?

(48–49) What kind of life reveals a person does not believe Christ will return?

(51) Where else does Jesus speak of weeping and gnashing of teeth?

Matthew 24:43-51

Notes

(1) How does a wedding serve as a fitting picture of Christ's second coming? (See Rev. 21–22.)

(3–4) What is the difference between the wise and foolis virgins?

(5) Who is the bridegroom? (See 9:15.)

(8–9) What does oil symbolize in Scripture? (See 1 Sam. 16:1

Matthew 25:1-10

Notes

(12) Why would Christ say He did not know them though they said, "Lord, Lord"? (See 7:21–23.)

(14–15) How does this represent Christ's first coming an His kingdom today?

(16–17) What do the talents teach about our responsibility to the Lord?

Notes

(20–23) How should this hope give Christians joy and energy to serve Christ?

Matthew 25:18-23

Notes

(24–25) What is the third servant's view of the Lord? How does it affect his service?

(28–30) What is the Lord's judgment on the third servar

Matthew 25:24-30

Notes

(31) What does this teach about Christ's second coming?

(32) Why does Christ compare Himself here to a shepherd? (See Ezek. 34:17.)

(34) What promise did Christ give to His sheep?

Matthew 25:31-39

Notes

(40) What are some distinguishing marks of a true sheep of Christ?

(41) What threat did Christ make against the wicked?

(45) What are some distinguishing marks of those who do not belong to Christ?

(46) What does this teach about heaven and hell?

Matthew 25:40-46

Notes

(2) What is the Passover? (See Ex. 12:3–13.) Why was Jesus crucified at that time? (See 1 Cor. 5:7.)

(5) Why did the priests want to avoid arresting Jesus then? (See 21:46.)

(7) What did this gift reveal about the woman's heart?

Matthew 26:1-9

Notes

(10) How did Christ respond to criticisms against the woman

(12) Why did the woman pour out the ointment then?

(14–15) Why did Judas betray Jesus? (See John 6:70–71; 12:4–6.)

Notes

(18) What did Christ mean by, "my time is at hand"? (See v. 45.)

(21) What does the Lord's knowledge of the future reveal about Him? (See John 13:19.)

(24) How does this verse imply both God's sovereignty an[d] man's responsibility?

Notes

(26) How did the Lord Jesus change the Passover meal i[n]
the Lord's Supper?

(28) What did Christ teach about the reason for His deat[h]

(31) What scripture is quoted here?

(33) What does Peter's answer show about him?

Notes

(34) How could Christ know the details of what Peter would do in the future?

(39) What is the cup that Jesus is praying about? (See Isa. 51:17.)

Notes

(42) How does "Thy will be done" display the greatness o[f]
Christ's obedience?

(44) Why does Jesus offer the same prayer three times?

(47) What do the size and equipment of the crowd imply
about what the priests expected?

(49) How did Judas betray the Lord? What does this sh[ow]
about him?

Notes

(53) What could Christ have done to stop His arrest?

(54) Why did Christ not resist arrest?

(56) Why does Matthew emphasize that all this fulfilled the Scriptures?

matthew 26:50-56

Notes

(59) How concerned were the priests about the truth?

(63) How did the Lord respond to these false accusations
(See Isa. 53:7.)

Matthew 26:57-63

Notes

(64) What did Jesus confess about Himself? (See Ps. 110:1; Dan. 7:13–14.)

(67) What abuse did the Lord endure? (See Isa. 50:6.)

(70) Why did Peter deny knowing Jesus?

Notes

(73) How did Peter's speech show he was Christ's discip
(See Luke 22:59.)

(74) Why does Peter's swearing an oath aggravate the seriousness of his sin?

Matthew 26:72-75

Notes

(2) Look up Pontius Pilate. Who was he? (See Luke 3:1; 13

(4–5) How did Judas's betrayal of Christ later affect hi

(6) What is ironic about them not putting this money in
treasury?

Notes

(11) What does it mean to be the king of the Jews?

(14) How does Christ demonstrate His meekness?

Notes

(18) Why did the priests desire to kill Jesus?

(22) Crucifixion involved being hung upon a wooden pole made from a tree. (See Acts 5:30.) How is this a sign of what happened spiritually when Christ was dying? (See Deut. 21:22–23; Gal. 3:13.)

Matthew 27:17-23

Notes

(24) Why did Pilate wash his hands?

(26) How does the release of a lawbreaker and the sentencing of Christ to death picture the gospel?

(29) Why are thorns fitting as Christ dies for fallen me

(See Gen. 3:17–19.)

Notes

(34) How did this fulfill the Scriptures? (See Ps. 69:21.)

(35–46) List all the ways these events fulfilled Psalm 2

Notes

(45) What did the darkness signify? (See Ex. 10:21–23; Isa. 13:9–10; Joel 2:31.)

(46) How and why was Jesus forsaken by God? (See 2 Cor. 5:21.)

0

2

3

4

5

6

Notes

(51) What is the significance of the veil being torn? (See Heb. 10:19–22.)

(53) Why did God raise some people from the dead?

7

2

3

4

Notes

(55) What does the presence of these women suggest abo
them?

(60) How does Christ's burial by a rich man fulfill prophec
(See Isa. 53:9.)

Matthew 27:55-62

5

6

7

8

9

0

2

Notes

(63) Why did the priest and Pharisees secure a unit of soldiers from Pilate?

(66) How did they secure the tomb from tampering?

Matthew 27:63-66

3

4

5

6

Notes

(1) Why do the Gospels emphasize that this was the first day of the week?

(2–4) How do these events compare to God's coming to Mount Sinai? (See Ex. 19:16–18.)

(6) Why did the angel invite the women to see the empty tom

(8) Why did they feel fear and joy?

(10) What would it have meant to the disciples who had a
failed Christ (26:31, 56) for the risen Lord to say, "Do n
be afraid," and to call them His brothers?

(13) What does the priests' response to the soldiers show
about their minds?

(16) What are some other significant mountains in the Bib

Notes

(17) Why did some of the disciples doubt when they saw Christ on the mountain in Galilee? Why do some believers struggle with doubt today?

(18–20) List both the promises and commands Christ gave His church. What part do you have in fulfilling the church's responsibility today?

Notes

Notes

Notes